COOKING WITH HERB
The Vegetarian Dragon

Grand-Pa-Pa-
Snap-Dragon

Grand-Ma-Ma-
Flora

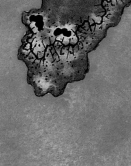

Herb

For Jeannine, who loves me and my cooking — J. B.
For Penny, Paul, Charles, Sara, Alex and Kate — D. H.

Barefoot Books
PO Box 95
Kingswood
Bristol
BS30 5BH

This book was typeset in FlareSerif and Nueva Roman
The illustrations were prepared in watercolour, crayon, pen and ink on thick watercolour paper

Graphic design by Tom Grzelinski, Bath
Colour separation by Grafiscan, Verona
Printed and bound in Singapore by Tien Wah Press (Pte) Ltd

This book has been printed on 100% acid-free paper

ISBN 1 84148 040 1

British Cataloguing-in-Publication Data: a catalogue record for this book is available from the British Library

1 3 5 7 9 8 6 4 2

Haggis

Hopper

Squat

COOKING WITH HERB
The Vegetarian Dragon
A Cook Book for Kids

Rosie-Rose

Meathook

Gorse

Text and recipes by
JULES BASS

Illustrations by
DEBBIE HARTER

Barefoot Books
Bath

Colander

Stockpot

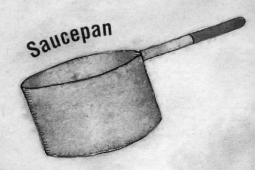
Saucepan

Sieve

Grater

Peeler

Blender & Processor

Garlic Press

Measuring Spoon

Measuring Cup

Electric Beater

Measuring Jug

CONTENTS

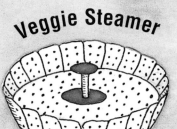
Veggie Steamer

Frying Pan

Sauté Pan

Ladle

Whisk

Wooden Spoon

Spatula

Cooks' Knives

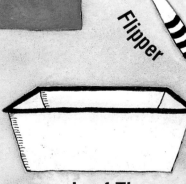
Flipper

Baking Tray

Pastry Cutters

Loaf Tin

Introduction

The recipes in this book are mainly for those I like to call **LOVE** children: **L**=lacto **O**=ova **V**=veggie **E**=eaters. This type of vegetarian diet is reasonable, well accepted and proven to be healthy for kids as well as for dragons like me.

My human friends tell me that the British Medical Association and the British Dietetic Association have both sanctioned the lacto-ova vegetarian diet.

A vegetarian could be described as someone who does not eat meat. Sometimes people call themselves vegetarians, but they eat fish. My philosophy is: whatever works. Kids who are thinking about becoming vegetarians don't have to do it overnight. They can take their time — get used to it, however long it takes.

Life isn't a race or a contest. On the way you may fall off the track *and even eat a piece of you-know-what!* No big deal! That doesn't make you a carnivore. And about your friends who don't want to be vegetarians? Hey, live and let live. Don't make them feel bad about it — and I hope they won't give you a hard time about how *you* want to eat!

A word about the recipes: some kids will be able to prepare them by themselves while others will need some help. Either way, I hope you kids *get involved* because cooking can be lots of fun. You get to eat what you've cooked-up. And wait until the first time you hear someone say: 'Hey, did you really make this? It tastes great!' It'll make you turn the page and try another of my recipes.

Remember, the recipes aren't just for kids — everyone can join in. Don't forget to let me know how your meal turns out.

Herb

How I Learned to Cook

My Grand-Ma-Ma-Flora was the best cook in our family — sorry, Mum! She gave me my first cooking lesson when I was six years old.

My cousin, Rosie-Rose, and my best dragon-pal, Gorse, were at the lair for lunch that day. We were going to make her famous *spaghetti sandwiches*. I could scoff a dozen of them and was dying to learn how to make them for myself.

'Now, dragon-littles, before we begin,' Grand-Ma-Ma-Flora said, 'you'll have to learn how to get everything you're going to cook with ready before you start. That's called "preparation". So, let's find all the ingredients — the foodstuffs you see in the recipe — and all the pots, pans and gadgets, so they'll be handy. Each one has a special use. *Can't boil spaghetti in a frying pan, you know!* Just remember: good cooks, like good workers, always use the right tools.

'Now, before we start, there are some safety rules:

1. Never try to catch a falling knife. You could cut yourself. Let it drop.
2. Always keep your knives sharp — a sharp knife doesn't slip.
3. Don't press hard on the knife until it's buried in what you're cutting.
4. Always keep your hands super-dry so nothing slips.
5. Always wear oven gloves when taking hot stuff out of the oven.
6. DON'T EVER RUSH — that's when you can hurt yourself.
7. Cook with the most important ingredient of all: LOVE!'

Grand-Ma-Ma-Flora took down a pile of utensils from her shelves and handed them out. I got a round metal bowl full of holes. 'Whatever would we use that for?' I thought.

'It's a colander,' said Grand-Ma-Ma-Flora, 'and it's used for draining water — like separating the spaghetti from the water you boiled it in.'

That sounded like fun! So I gave it a try.

MY FIRST COOKING LESSON

Because of what Rosie-Rose said about boy dragons not being able to cook, I was determined to show her I could cook with the best of them. This *Spaghetti Sandwich* was the first thing I ever tried to make, and it turned out delicious. It's still one of my favourite recipes. Don't brag about how easy it is. Let your friends think it's really hard to do!

Grand-Ma-Ma-Flora's *hard to make* Spaghetti Sandwich

▸ Here's what you'll have to hunt up: (Serves 2)

About 150gms leftover cold spaghetti (with the sauce mixed in it)
2 tablespoons good olive oil
2 whole eggs, beaten with salt and pepper

25gms grated Parmesan cheese
Sliced bread and butter

Preparation time: 15 minutes

Cooking time: 10 minutes

1 Turn on the grill to high. Put the rack about 10cm from the heat.

2 Put the olive oil in a non-stick frying pan on medium heat. Add the spaghetti. Turn with a wooden spoon until the spaghetti is warmed.

3 Pour on the eggs and cook for 30 seconds. Sprinkle the cheese over and slide the pan under the grill.

4 Grill until the eggs are firm and the *frittata* is lightly browned on top. Slide out on to a plate.

To Serve Pile a few slices of the *frittata* on to your favourite bread. You've done it! A first-class *spaghetti sandwich*. Good hot or at room temperature.

*pronounced free-*ta*-ta, which is what this dish is called in Italian

I can say it in Italian, 'Free ta ta!'

Herb's Hot Tips

Leave the door of the grill compartment open so that the handle of the frying pan sticks out. Pick it up with an oven glove.

Grand-Pa-Pa was known as the *Grand Snap Dragon*. Maybe that's because he was head of our dragon-clan, or maybe it's because he did tend to *snap* at dragon-folk. Now G.S. (as he was known to his friends) was a very fussy eater, so the first time he came to lunch I was a nervous wreck. I had decided to try out a new sauce for pasta (G.S. *loved* his pasta).

Hurry it up Herbie, dinner's already 5 minutes late!

Pasta and Sauce for a Grand Snap-Dragon

▼ Here's what you'll have to hunt up: (Serves 4)

500gms pasta (macaroni or penne)
100gms butter
1 tablespoon flour
Pinch of nutmeg or allspice
360ml single cream

100gms grated Parmesan cheese
25gms plain breadcrumbs
Salt and pepper (to taste)

Preparation time: 10 minutes

1 Melt the butter in a saucepan on a very low heat. Then add the flour and nutmeg and cook for 5 minutes. Stir from time to time with a whisk.

2 Add salt, pepper and the cream. Cook for 10 minutes, whisking from time to time (don't let it burn!). Then put the lid on the saucepan and take off the heat.

3 Pre-heat the oven to 230°C (Gas Mark 8). Bring a large spaghetti-pan of water to a boil, add a tablespoon of salt and throw in the pasta. Boil until

Cooking time: 50 minutes

firm to the tooth — we call that *al dente* (al-<u>den</u>-tay) in Italian.

4 Warm up the sauce. Put the pasta in a baking dish and pour ²/₃ of the sauce and half of the cheese over it. Mix well. Pour the rest of the sauce on top and sprinkle with the remaining Parmesan and breadcrumbs. Bake for 10 minutes.

To Serve Put the baking dish on the table (on a heat-proof mat) and spoon on to warmed plates.

G.S.'s Hot Tip

If the sauce looks too thick, thin it down with some milk. It gets thicker as you cook it.

11

When Grand-Ma-Ma-Flora said, 'Today, we'll make a pan bread,' Gorse and I said, 'No way. Too difficult.' Only Rosie-Rose agreed to try. Well, when it was done, we felt silly — it looked so easy. Not only that, the smell of fresh bread attracted a crowd, and I didn't even get a taste. 'Serves you right,' said Rosie-Rose, 'for not trying.' So I grabbed some flour and had a go. It really was easy! Now, I bake it all the time.

Rosemary Pan Bread

▶ Here's what you'll have to hunt up: (Serves 4)

350gms strong flour
1 teaspoon salt
3 teaspoons dried yeast granules (or 8gms fresh yeast)
¹/₂ teaspoon sugar

7 tablespoons olive oil
250ml warm water ('baby bottle' warm)
2 tablespoons chopped rosemary

Preparation time: 90 minutes

Cooking time: 15 minutes

1 Put the yeast and sugar in the water and stir until it dissolves. Let it sit for 5 minutes.

2 Combine the flour and salt in a mixer or food processor (with a steel blade). Add 2 tablespoons of olive oil to the water. Turn on the machine and slowly add the water mix to the flour. Stop the moment it forms a ball. Scrape it on to a floured surface and knead with floured hands until smooth (about 5 minutes or more).

3 Put the ball of dough in a bowl to rest. Cover the bowl with cling film and leave until the dough doubles in size (30-40 minutes).

4 Take the dough out of the bowl and punch it down — but don't knead it. Put it in the centre of an oiled baking tray about 23cm x 30cm x 1¹/₂cm. Cover with a teatowel.

5 Pre-heat the oven to 190°C (Gas Mark 5). After ten minutes, roll (or press out) the dough until it almost covers the bottom of the tray (neatness does not count here!). Cover with the towel and let it rest for 10 minutes.

6 Paint the dough with olive oil, sprinkle on the rosemary and extra salt and bake until golden (about 15 minutes).

To Serve Cool on a rack. Slice into squares. Eat while it's warm.

Look what I've made!

Rosie's Hot Tip

If the dough is too sticky, add a bit of flour. If it's too dry, add a bit of water until it's right.

I remember how we tricked Meathook into eating my famous chili. 'How can you make chili without meat?' he bellowed. 'It's Chili CON Carne, isn't it? Even I know that "CON carne" in Spanish means "WITH meat". You won't fool me with this one.' Then he said he liked it hot, so I added an extra scoop of chili powder. I'm telling you, it was **flame-out hot** — and, of course, meat-less, but he never knew the difference!

Herb's Chili Con 'No' Carne

▸ Here's what you'll have to hunt up: (Serves 4)

120gms textured vegetable protein (TVP)
500ml vegetable stock
1 large onion, chopped
2 garlic cloves, pressed
1 small tin tomatoes, chopped
1 small tin red pinto beans, drained

2 tablespoons cumin powder
1 teaspoon dried oregano
2 tablespoons sunflower or olive oil
Chili powder (to taste)
Salt and pepper (to taste)
Grated cheese, to garnish

Preparation time: 15 minutes

Cooking time: 25 minutes

1 Warm the oil in a frying pan on a low heat. Add the garlic, cook for a minute, then add the onions. Let 'em get golden (don't burn the stuff).

2 Dump in the tomatoes. Stir and cook for 10 minutes, uncovered. Add the cumin, oregano, salt, pepper and chili powder (you can always add more later — don't get it *too* hot!). Stir, add the stock, and stir again.

3 Mix and cook for 5 minutes

and throw in the TVP. Mix and add the beans. Mix again and put a lid on. Cook for five minutes and then taste. More salt? More chili powder? It's up to you. *You're* the chef!

To Serve Dish it up in small warmed bowls. Add some grated cheese and you've done it. Great *Chili Con 'No' Carne!* (con means 'with' and carne means 'meat' in dragon-ese — also in Spanish!)

Herb's Hot Tips
Add more stock if it looks too dry. Try a spoonful of sour cream and some chopped coriander on top!

EASY BURRITOS
Warm some flour tortillas in a frying pan for 5 seconds on each side. Fill with *Chili Con 'No' Carne* and roll up. Top with cheese and sour cream.

Get your tongue into this one and join the *Gorse Chowder-Head Club*. He has his own cornfield and always brings over the first-picked ears and *begs* me to turn them into chowder. Hey, it's easy! You can do it too. Did you know that all dragons are corn-on-the-cob lovers? Don't you believe me? Well, next time you have a dragon to dinner, serve him an ear (of corn!) and see what happens!

SLURP! Smells goood

Wow, a compliment!

Herb's Chowder for Chowder-Heads

▸ Here's what you'll have to hunt up: (Serves 6)

8 ears of fresh corn-on-the-cob
½ onion, chopped fine
30gms butter
Some milk (about 500ml)
2 tomatoes, peeled, seeded and chopped
2 tablespoons chopped coriander

A bunch of fresh chives
1 lime (or lemon), cut in four pieces
Spices: ¼ teaspoon each of: ground cumin, hot chili powder, ground ginger, ground coriander seed, black pepper

Preparation time: 20 minutes

Cooking time: 20 minutes

1 Boil the corn for 4 minutes, drain and cool. Cut off the kernels from 5 ears and put them in a blender. Add enough milk to cover the corn and whizz for 1 minute.

2 Put the chopped onion in a small frying pan with butter and cook slowly until the onion is softened. Add to the blender.

3 Whizz for 30 seconds. Put the corn mix in a saucepan, add all the spices and stir.

4 Add the whole kernels from the last 3 ears. Cook over a low heat, covered, for 5 minutes. Add enough milk to make it soupy.

To Serve Serve in warm bowls. Snip some chives over each with scissors. Add the chopped cold tomatoes and a squeeze of lime (or lemon). It's a knock-out. (You can leave out or use less hot pepper, if you like.)

Gorse's Hot Tip

If you can't get fresh corn-on-the-cob, frozen kernels will work — but don't use tinned sweetcorn for this recipe.

Grand-Pa-Pa-Snap-Dragon told me the story of Stone Soup. There are many versions, but most tell the story of two travellers who stop at a poor village, light a fire and begin to cook a stone in a pot of water. The villagers feel sorry for the homeless men and everyone offers a vegetable to add to the pot. A delicious soup is created because all have shared what little they had. I hunted up a fine, large stone and Grand-Pa-Pa shared *his* recipe with me.

Is this one OK? It's my pet rock!

As long as it's bigger than your mouth!

Snap-Dragon's 'Stone Soup'

▼ Here's what you'll have to hunt up: (Serves 6)

One big, clean stone
200gms tiny dried macaroni
500gms borlotti (or similar) beans
A stalk of celery, peeled and chopped
2 small tomatoes, peeled, seeded and chopped
A small bunch of parsley, chopped
2 garlic cloves, pressed

1 large carrot, scraped and chopped
Olive oil (to taste)
Bunch of fresh basil
Grated Parmesan cheese
Salt and pepper (to taste)
Dragon lake water (or tap!)

Preparation time: 20 minutes

Cooking time: 45 minutes

1 Put the stone in a large saucepan. Add water to cover it by 7cm. Boil for 1 minute. Add the beans, celery, parsley, tomatoes, splash of olive oil, garlic and carrot. Cook on a low heat for 30 minutes. Put a ladleful of soup in a blender and whizz for 10 seconds. Pour back into the pot. Add salt and pepper. Cook for 10 minutes more.

2 Boil up the tiny pasta in lots of salted water. When it's

cooked (not too soft!), drain it and add to the soup. If it looks too thick, add a bit of pasta cooking water so it's soupy.

3 Put the basil in a blender. Whizz for 10 seconds with 50ml of olive oil and a teaspoon of salt.

To Serve Ladle the soup into warm bowls and dribble on some basil oil and a sprinkle of grated Parmesan cheese.

Herb's Hot Tips

Boil *dried* beans in water for 10 minutes. Let them sit off the heat for 30 minutes. Drain and add to the main pot at Step 1.

GORSE GOES MEXICAN

My pal Gorse has this dead-easy way of making what he calls 'Mexican Grilled Cheese Sandwiches'. They're very tasty. He likes to cut them into quarters and spoon on *Herb's Radical Dragon Salsa*. I like 'em with a spicy tomato salsa, too. Of course, I know how to make tortillas from scratch, but you'll want to buy yours in a packet at the market. You'll see that I changed the name to make it more authentic!

Dragonian Quesadillas

▼ Here's what you'll have to hunt up: (Serves 2-4)

12 flour tortillas (tor-<u>tee</u>-yahs)
Cheddar cheese
Peanut oil

FOR A SPICY TOMATO SALSA
300gms seeded and diced tomatoes

2 tablespoons diced red onion
Chili powder (to taste)
1 teaspoon salt
Juice of 1 lime (or lemon)
2 tablespoons chopped coriander
1 teaspoon cumin powder

Preparation time: 15 minutes

Cooking time: 12 minutes

1 Preheat the oven to 190ºC (Gas Mark 5). Lay six tortillas on a baking tray and cover with grated cheese (as much as you like).

2 Cover all six with the rest of the tortillas, paint each (using a brush) with a thin coat of the oil and bake for 10-12 minutes until the tops are lightly browned and crisp.

3 *For the Spicy Tomato Salsa* Really easy: mix all of the stuff together in a bowl and let it stand for 5 minutes.

To Serve Cut each tortilla into quarters and serve with a bowl of the salsa on the side. Eat with your claws — whoops, I mean *fingers!*

How come you changed the name to Kay Sa Whatever?

Gorse's Hot Tips

For a fuller meal, add some cooked, sliced mushrooms along with the cheese and serve with *guacamole*.

Try ordering a grilled cheese sandwich in a Mexican restaurant!

He's got a point - KAY SA DEE YAH!

GUACAMOLE

Peel an avocado, cut it up roughly, pour the juice of a lime (or lemon) over it and mix. Add a diced tomato, 2 tablespoons of diced onion, 2 tablespoons of chopped coriander, some salt, hot chili pepper (optional) and mix it all up with a fork.

I couldn't believe my ears when Meathook invited me to a dinner party for all his dragon pals — saying everyone was going to bring a dish. He asked me to prepare the main course and dessert, and would I bring some salad items from my garden? As he left he shouted, 'Don't forget the salad dressing, Veggie-Head!' Something told me I was being taken advantage of, but never mind — he *did* invite me.

Party Pasta for a Herd of Dragons

But Herb had to cook <u>all</u> the food!

▾ Here's what you'll have to hunt up: (Serves 6 or 10 as a side dish)

450gm of dried pasta shells (butterfly shapes are nice)
150gms cooked broccoli florets
4 tomatoes, chopped
12 sun-dried tomatoes (24 halves!) in oil, chopped
100gms fresh or defrosted peas

1 small red onion, chopped fine
1 tablespoon dried oregano
2 tablespoons vinegar
125ml olive oil
2 garlic cloves, squished
Salt and pepper (to taste)
About 12 fresh basil leaves

Preparation time: 25 minutes

Cooking time: 30 minutes

1 Fill a stock pot $^2/_3$'s with water and bring to the boil. Add one tablespoon of salt and the dried pasta. Taste at the 10-minute mark to see if it's done.

2 In a sauté pan or frying pan, add 50ml of olive oil and the garlic. Turn the heat to low and cook until the garlic is golden.

3 Drain the pasta in a colander, pour hot water over it and put it in a large bowl. Pour the olive oil and garlic mixture over it and mix. Add all the other ingredients and mix.

To Serve Tear up some basil with your fingers and sprinkle it over as you sing your favourite song really loud!

You want MORE?

Herb's Hot Tips

Do not refrigerate or the pasta will stick together!

ANYBODY CAN COOK POTATOES

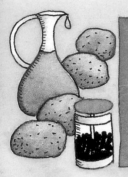

I discovered that there are entire books written about how to cook potatoes! Wow! Everyone has his or her favourite place to go for chips, since they're best from the chippy. So, let's forget about cooking them *that* way. My favourite recipe is really simple, but sometimes simple is best. I call them 'amazing' because that's what everyone says when I serve them.

Herb's 'Those Amazing Potatoes'

► Here's what you'll have to hunt up: (Serves 4)

4 large red-skinned potatoes
4 tablespoons olive oil

Salt and pepper (to taste)

Preparation time: 25 minutes

1 Scrub the potatoes, then put them in a saucepan filled with water and boil for about 20 minutes until they are done *but still firm* (a knife should go through rather easily).

2 Put the potatoes in a colander and let them dry and cool.

3 Pre-heat the oven to 205ºC (Gas Mark 6). Put 1 tablespoon of olive oil in a baking dish. Slice the potatoes thickly and scatter (overlapping) in the dish. Pour the other 3

Cooking time: 20 minutes

tablespoons of olive oil over the potatoes and add salt and pepper. Pop the dish into the oven for about 15-20 minutes.

4 *Peep in the oven from time to time*. When the slices are lightly golden in the centre and browning round the edges, take them out.

To Serve Serve with veggie burgers or loads of other vegetables.

I've had better. They're not THAT amazing.

You've eaten three portions!

Herb's Hot Tip

Don't peel the potatoes: the skins have lots of nutrients in them and are also very tasty.

Don't say 'Who ever heard of a dragon who spoke French?' What language do you think dragons who live in France speak? Ever since Rosie-Rose learned to *par-lay fran-say*, she's been cooking French dishes. I love soup, so I asked her to make a French soup. Next day she swooped into my garden, made off with some leeks, onions, potatoes and chives and left a note saying lunch was at 1pm. I was late, the soup got cold and Rosie was cross, but...

Zut! La soupe c'est froid!

Cold, but good! Very good, Rosie!

Rosie-Rose's French
because of Herb
'Cold' ^ Potato Soup

▾ Here's what you'll have to hunt up: (Serves 4-6)

3 large potatoes, peeled and chunked
4 leeks (white part only), sliced
1 large onion, diced
1500ml water

500ml milk
50gms butter
Salt and pepper (to taste)
Bunch of fresh chives

Preparation time: 15 minutes

Cooking time: 30 minutes

1 Put a large saucepan over a low heat and add the butter. As soon as it melts, add the leeks and onion. Put a lid on and let it cook for 5 minutes.

2 Add the potatoes and water and mix with a wooden spoon. Let it cook slowly on a low heat until the potatoes can be pierced easily with a fork.

3 Add salt and pepper and allow it to cool to room temperature.

4 Put the soup into a food processor or blender a little at a time and purée (which means to blend until smooth).

5 Pour into a jug or bowl. Mix in enough milk to make it soupy and leave in the refrigerator until cold.

To Serve Pour into bowls and snip chives over each. Even a kid can do it right the first time! *C'est facile!* (Say-fah-<u>seal</u>) which means: *It's easy!*

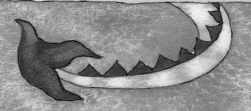

Rosie's French Tip

Try the French words:
Zut! La soupe c'est froid
Zoot! La-Soop-Say-Fwah
(*Drat! The soup is cold*)

Boy, was I surprised to get a visit from the Royal Chef of the Kingdom of Nogard. 'Herb,' he said, 'the King and Queen have decided to become vegetarians. Problem is, I know nothing about vegetarian cooking — so, I was hoping you'd give me a recipe to replace the King's favourite, *Wild Boar-Burgers*. I tried a veggie version yesterday and the Royal Taster spat it out! I'm in big trouble, Herb.' I think the recipe I gave him saved his neck!

The King's Favourite Veggie-Burger

▼ Here's what you'll have to hunt up: (Makes 4)

60gms fine textured vegetable protein (TVP)
1 carrot, scraped
1 large mushroom, chopped
1 small onion, roughly chopped
½ small red sweet pepper, roughly chopped

1 garlic clove, squashed
3 tablespoons cooking oil
2 egg whites and 1 egg yolk
25gms breadcrumbs
250ml hot water
Salt and pepper (to taste)
Hamburger buns and ketchup

Preparation time: 25 minutes

Cooking time: 15 minutes

1 In a food processor, shred one carrot. Put a knife attachment in the processor bowl and add the mushroom, onion and pepper. Turn on the machine and run it until the mixture's all ground up.

2 Pour 2 tablespoons of cooking oil into a saucepan. Add garlic and cook on a low heat. Then add the contents of the processor bowl. Add salt and pepper.

3 Cook for 10 minutes on a low heat, stirring every few minutes. Put the TVP in a

small bowl and add the hot water. Stir and cover. Let it sit for 5 minutes.

4 Off the heat, add the TVP and breadcrumbs. Cool for 5 minutes and mix in the eggs. Form into 4 (9cm) burgers and refrigerate for half an hour.

5 Put one tablespoon of cooking oil into a frying pan. Over a medium-high heat, cook the burgers for 5 minutes on each side.

To Serve On toasted buns, with ketchup.

TVP? What does that stand for?

The King's Hot Tip

I like my burgers with a slice of onion. To make it sweet, my chef soaks it in water and ice cubes for half an hour.

I was having a party and wanted to serve a heap of veggies in a fun way along with a pasta dish. I got the idea from my sailboat, the *S.S. Courgette*. I made Grand-Ma-Ma-Flora's delicious *Veggie Ra-ta-too* and spooned it into scooped-out courgette halves. When I cut out the sails, I put names on them with crayons. They tell everyone where to sit and they look great, too.

Veggie Sailboats

▼ Here's what you'll have to hunt up: (Serves 4)

4 long fat courgettes
1 red pepper, chopped
1 onion, chopped
1 small aubergine, chopped
2 tomatoes, seeded and
  chopped
12gms breadcrumbs
25gms grated cheese

1 tablespoon olive oil
1 garlic clove (optional),
  pressed
1 teaspoon oregano
Salt and pepper (to taste)
White paper
Wooden skewers

Preparation time: 30 minutes

Cooking time: 15 minutes

1 Cut all the courgettes in half lengthways and scrape out the seeds with a spoon (they should now look like dugout canoes!).

2 Put the olive oil in a small saucepan. Add garlic and turn the heat to low. Cook for one minute and add the onion and pepper. Mix and cook for 5 minutes. Add the aubergine. Mix. Cook for 4 minutes. Add the tomatoes and oregano. Mix. Cook for 5 minutes.

3 Add salt and pepper and spoon into the courgette 'boats'. Sprinkle the

breadcrumbs and cheese over each and drizzle some extra olive oil over them.

4 Preheat the oven to 190°C (Gas Mark 5). Place the boats in a baking dish and bake for 15 minutes or until lightly browned on top. If the boats have been refrigerated, allow them to come to room temperature before baking.

To Serve Make a sail by cutting out a large triangle from a piece of white paper. Fold it in half and tape it round a wooden skewer. Stick it in the boat where a sail should be.

Herb's Hot Tip

If you put the boats in the refrigerator before cooking them, be sure to cover them with some cling film or foil.

When I make these fritters I have to remember to save some batter for myself. Gorse and Rosie-Rose can scoff 'em as fast as I make them — slathered with golden syrup or just plain. I know they're good because ol' Meathook (who can't boil water!) sent one of his dragon pals to ask for (*steal*) the recipe.

Herb's Crunchy Corn Fritters

▸ Here's what you'll have to hunt up: (Serves 4)

300gms sweetcorn kernels (frozen)
2 large eggs
50gms self-raising flour

Peanut oil for frying
Salt and pepper (to taste)

Preparation time: 20 minutes

Cooking time: 15 minutes

1 Cook frozen sweetcorn kernels according to the packet instructions. Don't cook tinned sweetcorn. Put ⅔'s of the sweetcorn kernels in a blender and whizz for 15 seconds.

2 Add one whole egg and one yolk. Keep the other egg white in a bowl. Season the blender stuff with salt and pepper. Turn on the blender and add 1 tablespoon of oil, then add the flour slowly. This is your batter. Put it in a bowl and add the rest of the sweetcorn kernels.

3 Beat the egg white until it is fairly stiff and add to the batter, mixing in with a spatula.

4 Add 250ml of oil to the frying pan and heat on medium until the oil is hot (but not smoking). Add the batter by tablespoonfuls — flatten them a bit — and fry on both sides until dark golden.

To Serve Drain on absorbent paper and serve. Don't forget the golden syrup! (I like to heat it up.)

We need that recipe!

No way, meatbrain.

Herb's Hot Tips

Don't let the oil get smoking hot (your fritters will turn black). Add extra oil for the second batch; remove any burned chunks.

The old millstones, turned only by the movement of water from a stream, grind all the flour the townspeople and we dragons use to make bread. The stones also grind Gorse's dried corn-on-the-cob into a gritty corn-flour that cooks up into a dish called *polenta*. Grand-Ma-Ma-Flora taught Gorse to make it in two different ways: as a creamy side-dish (instead of mashed potatoes) and also formed into circles which she fried. Yum!

Flora's Crispy Polenta Circles (Made with Gorse's corn)

▼ Here's what you'll have to hunt up: (Serves 6-8)

500gms polenta cornmeal flour
125gms corn-on-the-cob kernels (fresh or frozen)

1 tablespoon salt
1.6ls water
3 tablespoons cooking oil

Preparation time: 30 minutes

Cooking time: 10 minutes

1 Cook the fresh corn-on-the-cob kernels in boiling water for 4 minutes. Cook the frozen corn kernels according to the packet directions.

2 Put the water in a saucepan and bring to the boil. Add the salt. Slowly add the polenta in a thin stream while mixing with a wooden spoon. When it's all in, turn the heat down to low.

3 Keep mixing with the spoon until the polenta pulls away from the sides of the pot and is thick but still pourable (see HOT TIPS).

4 Mix in the corn kernels. Pour on to a board or baking sheet

and smooth with a wet spatula to make it 2cm or so thick. Cool to room temperature.

5 Cut circles with a biscuit-cutter about 7cm in diameter. You can put it in the fridge for a while at this point, or continue.

6 Put 3 tablespoons of cooking oil in a frying pan over a medium heat and fry the circles until golden and crispy on each side (peep underneath to check!).

To Serve Put on warm plates. You can pour over some golden syrup or a spoon of your favourite salsa (or Herb's Radical Salsa — see page 36)

Flora's Hot Tips
You can also serve the polenta when Step 3 is completed, adding a little milk to make it creamy like mashed potatoes.

29

DO DRAGONS EAT PIZZA?

Do you know where pizza was invented? Some say it started with Egyptian flat bread. Do you know what the Italian word *pizza* means? It's 'pie'. It started to be popular after the end of World War II when the idea was brought back by soldiers who had been in Italy. Do you know the first *dragon* to make a pizza? You got it! Ol' Herb. No one in the forest of Nogard had ever heard of it, 'till me! Amaze your friends with these dragon-scoops.

Herb's Sort-of ^Original Rainbow Pizza

▼ Here's what you'll have to hunt up: (Serves 4)

2 pizza bases (10")
¹⁄₂ green sweet pepper
¹⁄₂ yellow sweet pepper
2 large ripe tomatoes
2 mushrooms
3 tablespoons olive oil

125gms mozzarella cheese, sliced
1 teaspoon dried oregano
Salt and pepper (to taste)

Preparation time: 25 minutes

Cooking time: 15 minutes

1 Pre-heat the oven to 220°C (Gas Mark 7).

2 Cut the peppers along the natural indentations and cut out the white ribs, discarding the seeds. Slice the mushrooms. Cut the tomato in half, take out the seeds and cut again in chunks.

3 In a frying pan, add 2 tablespoons of olive oil and turn the heat to medium. Add all the peppers and cook, turning from time to time, until they are softened.

4 Arrange the peppers, tomato and mushrooms on the pizza in a colourful way, alternating stripes or in circles. Scatter the mozzarella around, sprinkle with oregano, salt, pepper and the rest of the olive oil. Pop it in the oven and bake until the crust is golden and crisp.

To Serve If you don't know how to serve pizza, I'm not going to tell you!

Needs a touch more oregano.

Royal Taster

Herb's Hot Tip
Don't put too much stuff on the pizza or it will get soggy. Better to save the ingredients for another day.

So many people and dragons have begged (hah!) for my special salad dressing recipe that I've finally given in and am printing it here for the first time! (Are you lucky, or what?) You'll find the 'secret' in my HOT TIP at the end of the recipe. While I was at it, I thought I'd also give you a few hints about how to make up a decent salad — something you should know.

For a jar of your secret salad dressing, the king will appoint you 'Dresser of the Royal Salad'.

Salads and Sweet 'n' Sour Dressing

▶ Here's what you'll have to hunt up:

For the Salad Dressing
2 tablespoons vinegar
1 tablespoon liquid sugar
   (see HOT TIP below)
A tiny bit of pressed garlic
1/2 teaspoon salt
10 grindings of pepper
10 tablespoons olive oil
Mix it all up with a whisk.

For the Salad
Mix up stuff you like from these lists:

GROUP A
Cos lettuce
Chicory

Radicchio
Lamb's lettuce
Endive
Rocket
Watercress

GROUP B
Tomatoes
Radishes
Avocado
Cucumber
Basil leaves
Very thin sliced red onion
Shredded sweet red pepper
Black olives
Shredded carrots
Cooked sliced beetroots

Preparation time: 15 minutes

Choose one or more ingredients from group A and group B and mix them together with enough salad dressing to coat everything — but don't make it soggy.

Herb's Hot Tip

The 'secret' is liquid sugar. Make it by cooking a cup of white sugar with a cup of white vinegar until the sugar dissolves.

Hey, when you're a seven-year-old dragon, you don't want to stand in front of a hot stove for half an hour, stirring a pot of rice. Not when all your friends are having a good time swimming in Nogard lake without you. Right? Don't cry, try making risotto (ree-<u>zoh</u>-tow), which is Italian for rice, *my way*. It's just baked rice. It's easy to make. You might like it!

Do I really have to stir this rice for half an hour?

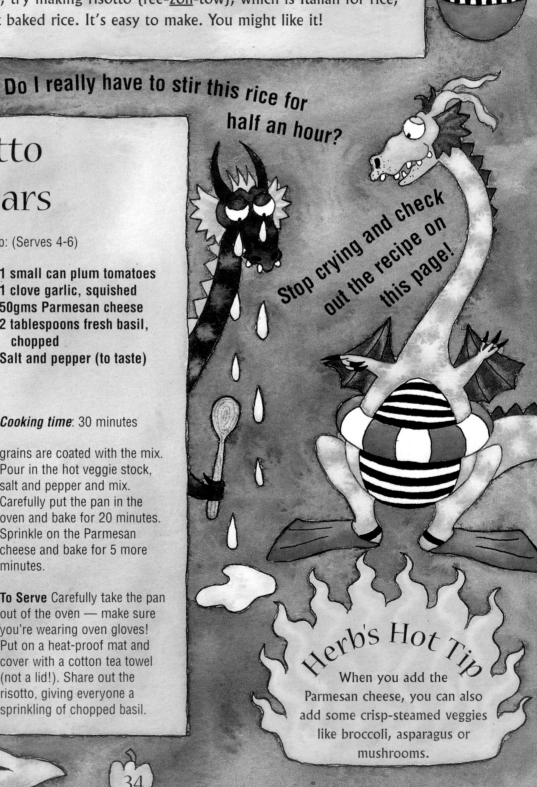

Stop crying and check out the recipe on this page!

Herb's Risotto Without Tears

▸ Here's what you'll have to hunt up: (Serves 4-6)

350gms long-grain rice
30gms butter
2 tablespoons olive oil
1 onion, minced finely
1 red pepper, seeded and
   minced
1000ml vegetable stock
¼ teaspoon turmeric

1 small can plum tomatoes
1 clove garlic, squished
50gms Parmesan cheese
2 tablespoons fresh basil,
   chopped
Salt and pepper (to taste)

Preparation time: 30 minutes

Cooking time: 30 minutes

1 Put the veggie stock and turmeric in a large pot to boil. Turn the oven to 190°C (Gas Mark 5). Toss the garlic, olive oil and butter in a large straight-sided 25cm sauté pan that can go in the oven. Cook on a low flame, stirring from time to time, for 2 minutes. Then add the onion and red pepper and mix. Cook for 5 more minutes. Add the chopped tomatoes and mix again.

2 Add the rice and stir with a wooden spoon until all the grains are coated with the mix. Pour in the hot veggie stock, salt and pepper and mix. Carefully put the pan in the oven and bake for 20 minutes. Sprinkle on the Parmesan cheese and bake for 5 more minutes.

To Serve Carefully take the pan out of the oven — make sure you're wearing oven gloves! Put on a heat-proof mat and cover with a cotton tea towel (not a lid!). Share out the risotto, giving everyone a sprinkling of chopped basil.

Herb's Hot Tip

When you add the Parmesan cheese, you can also add some crisp-steamed veggies like broccoli, asparagus or mushrooms.

Now, I've heard of sending flowers on Valentine's Day, but ones you can *eat*? That was a first for me. Rosie-Rose called them *Sweet Pepper Flowers* and they were as pretty as a picture — with petals of red, green and yellow. I must say, they were delicious. I grow the peppers (and the parsley) in my garden and I always have too much of both, so I was happy to learn a new way of using them.

Rosie-Rose's Sweet Pepper Flowers

▼ Here's what you'll have to hunt up: (Serves 4)

3 sweet peppers (red, yellow and green)
1 small bunch radishes
25gms white breadcrumbs
4 tablespoons chopped fresh parsley

1 garlic clove, pressed (optional)
1 tablespoon olive oil
¹/₂ teaspoon salt

Preparation time: 25 minutes

Cooking time: 15 minutes

1 Cut the peppers open along their natural rib indentations. Each pepper should give you about 6-8 long slices. Remove any seeds and hard white parts.

2 Boil some water in a large saucepan ²/₃ full. When the water boils, lower the heat to medium and add all the pepper slices. Cook for 3 minutes and drain in your colander. Let them cool.

3 Mix all the other ingredients (except the radishes) to make a nice pasty mess and spoon

this equally on to the slices of peppers.

4 Oil a baking tray and place the peppers on it, filling side up. Bake in a preheated oven 190°C (Gas Mark 5) for 15 minutes.

To Serve Place the peppers on a round plate, alternating the colours in a circle (like forming the petals of a daisy). Cut the radishes into thin slices and make a circle of them in the centre of the flower. Serve at room temperature as a first course or side dish.

She loves me, she loves me not...

She loves me, she loves me not...

Rosie's Hot Tip

It's fun to draw your meals before you make them. I always do. Try it with some crayons and a piece of paper!

SALSA! SALSA! SALSA!

One day I decided to add a dollop of corn-on-the-cob salsa to Grand-Ma-Ma-Flora's *Crispy Polenta Circles*. At first she and Gorse turned up their noses at this unheard-of addition — but now they both love it! Hah! Do you know what the word *salsa* means? In Spanish, it's the word for *sauce*!

OLÉ!

Herb's Radical Dragon-Salsa

▼ Here's what you'll have to hunt up:

3 ears of fresh (or 200gms frozen) corn-on-the-cob
3 sun-dried tomatoes (6 halves!) in oil, chopped
2 tablespoons chopped coriander

3 tablespoons olive oil
1 tablespoon lime (or lemon) juice
Chili powder (optional — see HOT TIP)
Salt (to taste)

Preparation time: 15 minutes

1 Boil the fresh corn-on-the-cob kernels for 4 minutes. Drain and cool. Cook the frozen corn kernels according to the packet directions.

2 Cut off the kernels and put them in a bowl. Add all the other stuff and mix it up well.

That's all there is to it.

To Serve This salsa is great with *Herb's Crunchy Corn Fritters*, *The King's Favourite Veggie-Burger* and *Flora's Crispy Polenta Circles*. Or just with crisps! Super!

Herb's Hot Tip

For really HOT salsa, add some hot chili powder. But go easy. Remember, you can make it hotter but it's hard to make it milder!

THE COOKIE DRAGON

One Sunday, I awoke to find a plate of chocolate chip cookies in front of my lair. They were delicious! Each week I found more. Who was leaving them? The next Sunday, I hid in a tree. Soon, I saw a dark shadow. I pounced and held it tightly. 'Who are you?' I gasped. 'I'm the *cookie dragon*. Set me free!'. 'Only if you give me the cookie recipe,' I said. He had no choice but to reveal it.

I think *you're* the Cookie Dragon.

(How did she guess????)

Chocolate Chippers

▾ Here's what you'll have to hunt up: (Makes 24)

8 tablespoons sunflower
   oil/butter mix*
65gms caster sugar
65gms dark brown sugar
150gms plain flour
1 egg
1/2 teaspoon salt
1 teaspoon vanilla extract

1 tablespoon black treacle
1/2 teaspoon baking powder
100gms dark or milk
   chocolate bits
30gms broken pecans
   (optional)
25gms raisins (if you
   like 'em — I do!)

Preparation time: 25 minutes

Cooking time: 12 minutes

To make the Sunflower/Butter Mix: in a bowl, allow 4 tablespoons of butter to come to room temperature. Add 4 tablespoons of oil. Whizz in a blender until combined. Scrape the mixture out into a bowl.

1 Preheat the oven to 190°C (Gas Mark 5). Put all the dry ingredients in a large bowl: flour, baking powder, sugars, salt, chocolate bits and broken pecans. Mix with a big spoon. Mix all the wet ingredients in a small bowl: egg, vanilla, butter and black treacle.

2 Dribble the wet stuff on to

the dry stuff and mix with a spoon. You'll know you've finished mixing when you can't see any more flour in the bowl.

3 Put heaped tablespoons of the dough mix on to a non-stick baking tray, leaving some space between each cookie, and pat down lightly with your finger to make them roundish (neatness does not count!).

4 Slide them into the middle of the oven and bake for around 12 minutes.

To Serve Cool 'em, eat 'em. Make more!

Herb's Hot Tips

Why use the oil/butter mix? Because good eating habits start when you're young. It cuts down on butter and tastes great.

Bananas grew wild outside Meathook's cave — but he never ate any of them. Each year they rotted. One day Rosie-Rose asked him if she could pick some. 'Take 'em all,' he growled. 'I *hate* bananas.' Rosie-Rose asked me what I could do with them and I came up with this bread recipe. Meathook smelled it baking and scoffed it as fast as I could make it. Suddenly, he was a banana *lover!*

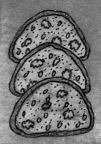

Meathook's Favourite

Chocolate Banana Walnut Bread

▼ Here's what you'll have to hunt up:

65gms sugar
3 tablespoons cocoa powder
1 egg
4 tablespoons sunflower oil
2 ripe bananas, fork mashed
225gms plain flour

1 tablespoon baking powder
$^1/_2$ teaspoon salt
12 walnut halves, broken up
60ml milk

Preparation time: 15 minutes

Cooking time: 1 hour

1 Preheat the oven to 180°C (Gas Mark 4). Put the sugar, salt, egg, sunflower oil and milk in a bowl with an electric mixer. Mix until all is well blended. Add the fork-mashed bananas and mix again on medium speed until they're well blended. Stop.

2 Add the flour, baking powder, cocoa powder and walnuts to the bowl and mix again until no white flour shows and it's all thick and creamy.

3 With a rubber spatula, scrape the dough into a non-stick loaf tin (about 23cm x 13cm x 8cm) which you have rubbed with a little bit of butter or oil.

4 Bake for 1 hour. Turn out on to a rack and let it cool.

To Serve Cut into slices and place on a plate, overlapping like a fan.

Keep 'em coming, Herb.

I thought you hated bananas?

Herb's Hot Tips

If you don't have a blender, you can make this by hand in a bowl with a wooden spoon and a whisk.

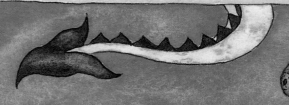

NO ONE WILL BELIEVE YOU MADE THIS

No one will believe you made it! Just tell 'em it's easy — when it's from Herb, the vegetarian dragon. Erm, maybe you'd better leave out the fact that I'm a dragon, unless your friends are very, you know, *advanced?* Hey, let me know how it turned out, okay? I think it's berry, berry good. Hah! If you have a better recipe, visit my personal website www.DragonHerb.com and send me an e-mail.

Herb's Simple Strawberry Slush

▶ Here's what you'll have to hunt up: (Serves 4)

250gms strawberries   **250ml water**
125gms sugar

Preparation time: Steps 1-3: 20 minutes + overnight freezing time
Step 4:   5 minutes

1 Making simple syrup is simple! Slowly cook the sugar with the water in a saucepan until the sugar dissolves. Boil it until you only have 150ml left (just over a third of what you started with) — takes about 10-12 minutes. Let it cool to room temperature before using.

2 Add the berries to a food processor fitted with a steel knife and pulse until the berries are chopped finely but not mushed!

3 Mix the berries and syrup in a glass bowl, then scrape into

a plastic container with a lid. Freeze overnight.

4 Set the bottom of the plastic container in hot water for a few seconds to loosen the slush. While still in the container, cut into small chunks with a blunt knife and plop into the processor. Whizz for a minute or less, until it's a creamy frozen yummy glob. Scrape down the sides and whizz for another 5 seconds.

To Serve Spoon into chilled glasses and serve with a berry on top.

Come on, get cooking with Herb!

Herb's Hot Tip

Start and stop the food processor. Scrape down the sides. Start and stop again until it looks like frozen sorbet.